www.raintreepublishers.co.uk
Visit our website to find out
more information about
Raintree books.

To order:
☎ Phone 0845 6044371
🖨 Fax +44 (0) 1865 312263
📧 Email myorders@raintreepublishers.co.uk

Customers from outside the UK please telephone +44 1865 312262

Raintree is an imprint of Capstone Global Library Limited,
a company incorporated in England and Wales having its
registered office at 7 Pilgrim Street, London, EC4V 6LB -
Registered company number: 6695582

First published by Raintree in 2013
The moral rights of the proprietor have been asserted.

Originally published by DC Comics in the U.S. in single
magazine form as Batman Adventures #3.
Copyright © 2012 DC Comics. All Rights Reserved.

Ashley C. Andersen Zantop *Publisher*
Michael Dahl *Editorial Director*
Donald Lemke & Sean Tulien *Editors*
Heather Kindseth *Creative Director*
Bob Lentz *Designer*
Kathy McColley *Production Specialist*
Printed and bound in China by Nordica.
051Z/CA21200799
DC COMICS
Joan Hilty *Original U.S. Editor*
Harvey Richards *U.S. Assistant Editor*
Bruce Timm *Cover Artist*

ISBN 978 1 406 25406 8
16 15 14 13 12
10 9 8 7 6 5 4 3 2 1

British Library Cataloguing in Publication Data
A full catalogue record for this book is
available from the British Library.

MY BOYFRIEND'S BACK

Ty Templeton & Dan Slott ....writers
Rick Burchett & Ty Templeton .... pencillers
Terry Beatty .... inker
Lee Loughridge & Zylonol Studios ....colorists
Phil Felix ....letterer

Batman created by
Bob Kane

VRRRR GLOOP!

EVIL, MAYBE... KNIEVEL... NOT SO MUCH. YOU'RE ZERO FOR SIX ON THAT JUMP, JOKER.

NO, NO! DON'T YOU GET IT, HONEY-BUN?

I DROVE A HALF-DOZEN MOTORCYCLES INTO A VAT OF TAPIOCA FOR YOU, SWEETIE!

IT'S A HARLEY PUDDING!

GET IT?!?

THINK OF THE MOTORCYCLES AS RAISINS!

IT'S NICE, I S'POSE...

BUT WHERE'S THE STYLE?

THE MAYHEM?

6

TAPPA TAPPA TAP TAP

PINKY McCONNEL?

AHH!

BATMAN!

BAD ENOUGH THAT YOU DO BUSINESS WITH A CRIMINAL MADMAN LIKE THE JOKER...

...BUT TO ADVERTISE "THE JOKER'S HELICOPTER" FOR SALE ON E-BUY... THAT'S JUST STUPID.

DO YOU KNOW WHAT IT'S WORTH?

IS IT WORTH YOUR LIFE?

LAST YEAR, I SOLD MATT HAGEN'S BEAT-UP OLD BUICK FOR FIFTY THOUSAND DOLLARS! THERE ARE COLLECTORS OUT THERE--

HOW MUCH DID JOKER PAY YOU? WHERE CAN I FIND HIM?

YOU **KNOW** WHERE HE IS.

I DON'T HAVE TO TELL YOU **ANY**-THING...

...YOU'RE A **WANTED** MAN.

I EVEN HEARD OUR MAYOR'S GOT A **PRICE** ON YOUR HEAD.

SIT DOWN AND **START** TALKING.

BLAM!

KLIK!

...AT THE CITY PRISON WHERE INMATES HAVE BEEN HOUSED FOLLOWING AN EXPLOSION AT ARKHAM ASYLUM, **ANOTHER** ESCAPE.

HERE'S **CAPTAIN RENEE MONTOYA** OF THE GOTHAM MAJOR CRIMES UNIT...

WE'RE STILL ASSESSING THE SITUATION HERE, SUMMER, BUT THE ATTACK SEEMED AIMED AT BREAKING OUT THE CAPTURED **ASSASSIN** FROM THE ARKHAM INCIDENT...

HECK NO! WELLL...*PROBABLY NOT*, ANYWAY...

I WANT YOU TO FINISH THE JOB--AND TRY TO KILL THE JOKER.

HON...?

DON'T WORRY, BABY...MY MONEY'S ON YOU, NO MATTER WHAT KIND OF *KUNG FU WHOOEY-WHAMMY* THING HE'S GOT GOING.

THE SURVIVAL INSTINCT IS THE *STRONGEST* IMPULSE YA GOT. AS SOON AS THE CHIPS ARE DOWN AND YOUR *LIFE* DEPENDS ON IT...

...YOUR NATURAL INCLINATION FOR *CHEATING*, *HURTING*, AND *FIGHTING DIRTY* WILL SAVE YOU...

...AND *I'LL* HAVE MY *OLD* JOKER BACK.

IF NOT-- --I PROMISE I'LL AVENGE YOU AND *MOIDER* THE BUM!

YOU...YOU'RE DOING THIS ALL FOR *ME*? WHAT A *GAL*!

IF I WAS YOU, MISTAH J...I'D *RUN*.

EEP!

12

WEEEE-HAA!

DON'T MAKE THIS DIFFICULT, AND I PROMISE I'LL BE QUICK.

RIGHT...

LIKE, HOW MANY TIMES HAVE I HEARD *THAT*?

PATHETIC...

WHA...?

YANK!

KLONG!

ZZWIP!

HARLEY *BABY!*

GOOD SHOT!

DO *YOU* KNOW HOW TO THROW A *PARTY!*

DON'T TOUCH ME.

I'VE HAD *ENOUGH* OF *YOU.*

C'MERE...

I GO FOR A MAN WITH *BIG* EARS.

SMOOCH!

WHAT...?

GET THIS *STRAIGHT*, YA *LUMMOX*-- I LIKE BATMAN BETTER THAN *YOU!* ALWAYS *DID!*

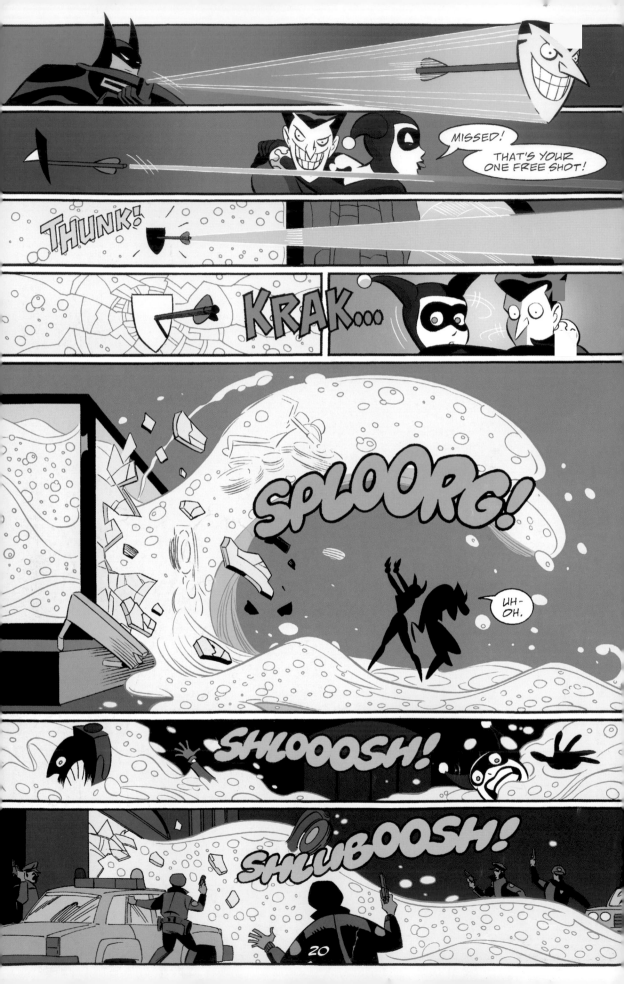

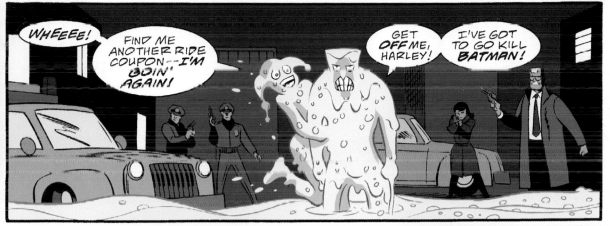

NEXT: RA'S TO THE FINISH!

CAREFUL! SHE COULD BE MAKING SOME KIND OF **POISON GAS** OR **SPORES** IN THERE!

WARD 7

LOOKS LIKE SHE'S DYING.

WHAT SHOULD WE DO?

KOFF

KOFF KOFF

WHAT YOU **SHOULD** DO, YA BIG **JOIKS**...

SMAK!

...IS LET HER **OUT!**

I GOTCHA, RED!

GASP!

WHAT... THEY'RE OKAY! THEY'RE... **LAUGHING?**

HA HA HA!

WHEEZ!

WHAT? IS IT SOME KIND OF **LAUGHING GAS?**

NO, IT'S...

hee hee hee!

26

CREATORS

TY TEMPLETON WRITER & PENCILLER

Ty Templeton was born in the wilds of downtown Toronto, Canada to a show-business family. He makes his living writing and drawing comic books, working on such characters as Batman, Superman, Spider-Man, The Simpsons, the Avengers, and many others.

DAN SLOTT WRITER

Dan Slott is a comics writer best known for his work on DC Comics' *Arkham Asylum*, and, for Marvel, *The Avengers* and the *Amazing Spider-Man*.

RICK BURCHETT PENCILLER

Rick Burchett has worked as a comics artist for more than 25 years. He has received the comics industry's Eisner Award three times, Spain's Haxtur Award, and he has been nominated for the Eagle Award. Rick lives with his wife and two sons in Missouri, USA.

TERRY BEATTY INKER

For more than ten years, Terry Beatty was the main inker of DC Comics' "animated-style" Batman comics, including *The Batman Strikes*. More recently, he worked on *Return to Perdition*, a graphic novel for DC's Vertigo Crime.

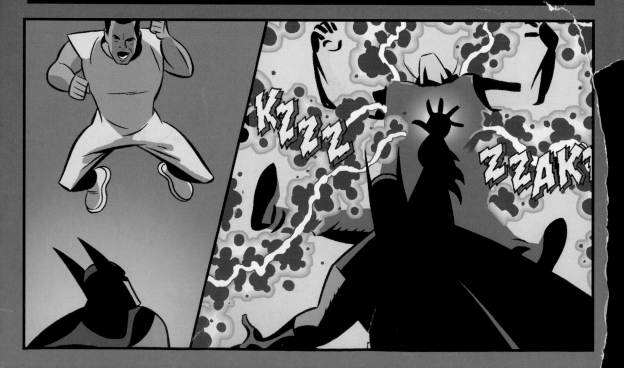

GLOSSARY

assassin person who kills another person, often for money

avenge to seek revenge for an action or on behalf of a person

aversion strong dislike

civilization advanced stage of human organization, technology, and culture

disciplines areas of study

homicidal of, relating to, or having tendencies toward the killing of another person

impulse sudden stirring up of the mind and spirit to do something

inclination feeling of liking or of wanting to do something

mayhem needless or willful damage or violence

mortar short muzzle-loading cannon used to fire shells at a low speed and at high angles

prowess great ability

taser weapon that delivers an electrical shock

BATMAN GLOSSARY

Arkham Asylum: a psychiatric hospital in Gotham City that often holds the world's most dangerous and insane criminals, such as the Joker, Scarecrow, Two-Face, and Scarface.

Captain Renee Montoya: captain of the Major Crimes Unit for the Gotham City Police Department.

Commissioner James Gordon: head of the Gotham City Police Department and a loyal friend of the Dark Knight.

Gotham City: Bruce Wayne's hometown.

Harley Quinn: Dr. Harleen Frances Quinzel is a Gotham City super-villain and the Joker's crazy girlfriend.

The Joker: one of Gotham City's worst super-villains and Batman's mortal enemy.

Ra's al Ghul: a centuries-old villain who hopes to save the world by killing most of humanity and ruling the few people who remain.

Society of Shadows: an organization of highly trained assassins led by Ra's al Ghul.

VISUAL QUESTIONS & PROMPTS

1. Comic book illustrators draw motion lines (also known as action lines) to show movement of a character or an object, like the knife in the panel below. Find other panels in this book with motion lines. Do you think they make the illustrations more exciting? Why or why not?

2. The Dark Knight is an expert martial artist. Find at least two panels in this book where Batman uses this skill. Do you believe he could've solved those problems differently? Explain your answer.

3. At the end of this story, Police Commissioner James Gordon pretends not to see Batman, even though the Dark Knight is standing right in front of him. Why do you think he lied about seeing the super hero?

3

4. The way a character's eyes and mouth look, also known as their facial expression, can tell a lot about the emotions he or she is feeling. Below, how do you think the Joker is feeling in each of the three panels? Use the illustration to explain your answer.

4

BATMAN ADVENTURES

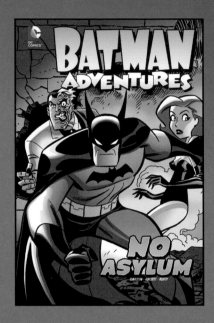

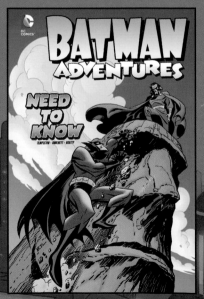

Raintree